Sula
and the
Franciscan Sisters

Sula, Parish Cat at Old Mission

Sula's amanuensis: Betty Lou Leaver

Copyeditor: Christine Campbell

Cover design: Carl D. Leaver and Opeyemi Ikuborije

Front cover photo of Sula and Sr. Maria del Rey: Betty Lou Leaver

Back cover photo of Sula and Sr. Delores: Robert Earl Groeling

Back cover photo of Sula: Stacey Gentry

Inside photographs: as marked

ISBN: 9781933455181

LCCN: 2022944765

Table of Contents

Introducing the Sisters, Their Convent Home and Work, and Our Mission

photograph by Silvia Rodriguez

1

photograph by Stacey Gentry

A long time ago, the Franciscan Sisters of the Atonement, as an order, were not Catholic; they were Anglican. Then, they became Catholic. As Franciscans, they found their way to Old Mission San Juan Bautista, a Franciscan Mission established by St. Junipero Serra and Franciscan friars from Mexico in 1797. The Franciscan sisters came later. Once here, they helped the parishioners, other people, the cats who came to visit them at the convent, like my friend Julius, and, of course, me.

The Franciscans are a mendicant order. That means that they work. Some orders are cloistered—they spend their time inside all the time, praying. Some orders teach; the

Jesuits like to teach. The Franciscans teach, too. The Franciscan Sisters of the Atonement at San Juan Bautista have taught at the St. Benedict School in nearby Hollister. They also have taught catechism, led the Rite of Christian Initiation of Adults program, and served as a source of information and inspiration for the Monday night bilingual prayer group. They know a lot; everybody at our Mission has learned a lot from them.

photograph by Jeanette Schneider

To understand the Franciscan Sisters of the Atonement, you have to know who St. Francis is because he was the great-great-great times many greats spiritual grandfather of our Mission and of the Sisters of the Atonement. They follow the Rule of St. Francis. The building of our Mission by the local Mutsun Indians (fun fact for Trekkies—their language is the basis for Klingon) was overseen by the Franciscans, who to this day follow the Rule of St. Francis. (The Rule reflects the guidelines that St. Francis wrote for his community in the 1200s, even before he was a saint.)

There are a lot of stories about St. Francis. You can read about some of them in my book, *Saints I Know*. Many other books about St. Francis tell other stories though perhaps some are more legend than true stories. One thing for sure, St. Francis liked nature and animals. I talked to him every morning after daily Mass in the Mission garden; it started my day out right.

I know that the Franciscan sisters talked to him a lot, too, though they may not have come and sat at his feet literally like I did. Figuratively, though…

So, this book is about a Franciscan Mission with Franciscan sisters, a Franciscan cat, and lots of Franciscan statues. I will share pictures of all of that with you in this book.

Remembering Me,
Sula

Photograph by Stacey Gentry

photograph by Stacey Gentry

I was like the sisters, in a way. You see, I was living in the San Juan Bautista (California) cemetery, then hanging out at City Hall.

9

While I was still a kitten, though, I heard the Mission bells ringing, and my little paws headed me across the way to the Mission. Here I found my forever home and my special mission to help the parishioners. So, I too, became a mendicant, like all the other Franciscans.

That is the summary. My whole story is quite a bit longer, but you can read about it in my other books. They are listed at the end of this book.

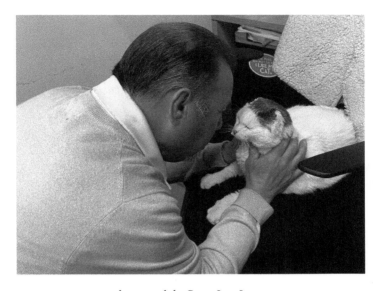

photograph by Betty Lou Leaver

I am a very lucky cat. I have had a lot of people take care of me.

The gift shop employees have always been there for me, from the very first day, especially Mary Anzar and Benito Garcia. (That is Benny with me in the picture.)

Over the years, many people have worked in the gift shop. Like the priests who have pastored the Mission, all the gift shop employees have been very kind to me.

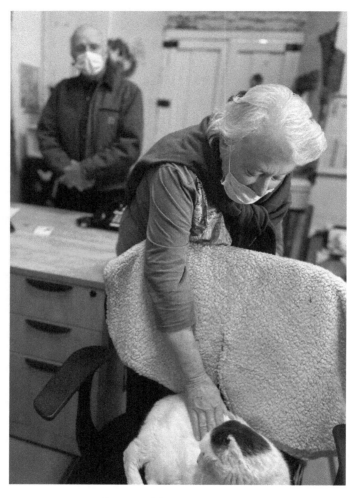

photograph by Betty Lou Leaver

Kris Maas, one of the parishioners, brings me sardines as a special treat from time to time. I like that. She even finds me when I am resting in my office in the back of the gift shop.

Other parishioners bring me treats, too. One brought me a warm house for sleeping outside safely in the winter when I was still living and working full-time at the Mission. Another purchased a pew in the church for me. Still others take pictures and share them; that way, it is easy to illustrate my books and share my "doings" on my Face Book page.

photograph by Betty Lou Leaver

Many drop by to say hello now that I cannot walk all the way to the church. Some pet me. Some pick me up so others can pet me. I sleep a lot now because it helps me forget about the pain from my cancer and also just because I am getting to be an old lady (around 15 years old now), but I do like to greet the parishioners either in the gift shop or in my office in the back of the gift shop.

When I was in the church for every Mass, many, many people petted me on their way out. Often, I would find someone who needed solacing and sit on that person's lap. And sometimes, I would be adopted as part of the family by parishioners, like the Mansmiths here, who would slide over so I could sit with them during Mass.

photograph by Jackie Smith

People have helped me with so many things, especially with my cancers. I have been through six bouts of various kinds of cancer, using up two-thirds of my nine lives pretty quickly.

Some people who help me are specialists. Others are just experienced cat caretakers or kind souls, which is equally important.

My vet in Hollister (you can read about him in my book, *Surviving Cancer, Healing People*) took care of me through several bouts of cancer. Then, my health became even more complicated and delicate. Now Dr. Arteaga at the Animal Cancer Center in Monterey has become my guardian oncologist.

My godmother takes me to see her and her team regularly. They have helped me through a couple new bouts of cancer and new kinds of cancer. That cancer just won't let go of me!

Dr. Arteaga and her team, pictured above (left to right: Maria, Dr. Teri Arteaga, Linda, Andrés, and Roberto), have helped me lot, really. They are always so kind to me, and Dr. Arteaga is very creative at finding ways to fight cancer and to make me feel better.

So, I am hanging on, dear readers. Really, I am though that can be difficult at times. (It helps having as many people as I do in my corner.)

photograph by Carol Andrijeski

Thank God for my godparents, Joe and Jackie Smith. They took me into their home after each of my surgeries.

Then, when Covid-19 came to visit, everyone had to run away and everything had to close down. The Mission closed, and Masses were streamed. That meant I had no one to visit with—no "mission" for a while, until some control measures were found to manage Covid. With the Mission closed, my home, the gift shop, also closed. Back I went to live with Joe and Jackie.

A little later, though the Mission re-opened, I retired (for reasons of age and health). Now, I live with the Smiths all the time and come to work on Sundays.

On Sundays, the Smiths bring me to the gift shop, where I still have my own "office" and rest area. There I get to meet all my old friends.

I wish I could meet them all again at Mass—I never used to miss a Mass—but, with growing tumors in my leg, I cannot walk that far. I am so happy to see my friends when they come to the gift shop.

I *am* still listed on the parish staff. People tell me, though, that they miss seeing me at the Mission all the time—just like they and I miss seeing the Franciscan sisters every day.

Times do change, but we do not lose the good times. We all hang onto them and store the good memories in our heads and hearts—and sometimes in a book!

photograph by Nicholas England

Here is a picture of me with my amanuensis. She visits me regularly, makes me feel comfortable, holds me for visitors to pet, and, of course, writes my books for me. If she finds out that I need something, either she helps or lets someone who can help know what I need.

photograph by Jeanne Wolverton

My amanuensis cannot handle the writing of my books all by herself. They have to be proofread. Here I am with Deacon Van who has copyedited most of my books and wrote part of the book on saints.

photograph by Betty Lou Leaver

From the time I came to Old Mission San Juan Bautista, the Franciscan Sisters of the Atonement were an important part of my life. Until August 2019, when I started to write this book (it sometimes takes me a long time to write a book—you know, paws are clumsy on typewriters), they lived here at the Mission with me, in the convent behind the Parish Education Center. They had a beautiful view of the valley, and though I never wandered as far as the convent itself, I often did wander out into the private driveway (in the picture) that separates the chapel, the education center, and the convent.

I could see where they lived, and I could see a fellow cat they kindly fed and watched out for: Julius. He did not have a forever home like I do. I was very happy that the sisters gave him some love and some food. Everyone, even cats, needs those things.

photograph from Graymoor website

Now the Franciscan sisters have left, retiring to their motherhouse in Graymoor. Although I cannot travel, some parishioners who are my friends have visited them and say that it is a lovely spot on the famous Hudson River across from the historic and still functioning West Point Military Academy.

Being a retiree myself now, I understand why they had to move into another stage of life, but they are missed very much. I wrote this book to commemorate how special they are and to say good-bye to them.

I especially want to share what I will remember about them—and what I hope they will remember about me and all the parishioners who love them at Old Mission San Juan Bautista.

As for me, well, I don't have a lot more to say about me because the sisters know me very, very well. So, I will just share some pictures in this book so that while they are far away from me in New York and I am still in California, they will remember me and the wonderful Old Mission San Juan Bautista that they loved together with me and the missions they undertook in support of it and its people—like I still do.

Remembering
Morning Mass

photograph by Betty Lou Leaver

photograph by Stacey Gentry

Every day when morning dawned, I quickly found my way to the entrance to the chapel, when morning Mass would soon begin. My life at the Mission among the Sisters started with daily Mass. I loved sharing the Presence of my Boss with them. (By the way, my Boss is also their Boss.)

I look forward to morning Masses with my friends and the sisters, like Rafael, Mary Ann, and Sr. Delores on the previous page.

Here I am, waiting for the door to be opened for morning Mass.

photograph by Betty Lou Leaver

Sometimes, Sr. June would come early and give me some treats. Yum!

photograph by Stacey Gentry

I eagerly waited for others to show up and invited them to come inside with me.

photograph by Studio Lovejoy

I did not always wait outside, though. In the cold months, once the doors were open, I quickly came inside and waited for my friends to show up.

photograph by Stacey Gentry

I would wait for a little while at the door, watching for people to come. If no one showed up right away, I would usually try to find my place for the Mass.

photograph by Stacey Gentry

I always tried to find one that had a good vantage point. That way, I could be comfortable and warm and still watch the door. People would always come; I just had to be patient.

photograph by Stacey Gentry

Here you can see how well I chose. No one could get past me without a morning greeting.

photographer unidentified

During Mass, once they arrived, I had many friends I could sit and worship with. Although I sat with the sisters much of the time, I also sat with others.

Here is Ed Degroot from the St. Francis Retreat Center at the top of the hill in San Juan Bautista. I know the Franciscan Sisters will remember him. He made music magic for our Masses.

photographer unidentified

And here I am with Jennie Watts, who takes pictures of me and does many more things for our parish. She took this picture with me.

photograph by Betty Lou Leaver

And here I am with my pal, Benito. Benny also spent many hours with the Franciscan Sisters because he worked at the Mission gift shop and at the parish office.

photograph by Betty Lou Leaver

At Mass, I always saw the sisters. Even if attendance was low, they were always there, like Sr. Delores with me here. One time, the priest had a problem at the last minute and was unable to come. Sr. Maria stepped in so that we could still have our readings and prayers. See how important the sisters were? I miss them!

photograph by Betty Lou Leaver

During Mass, I loved sitting with the sisters. It was just the most perfect place to be.

When Sr. Maria, who spent a couple of years away down south in San Ysidro with her own sister, returned, I would sit with her, too, as you can see from the cover of this book.

I loved them all: Sr. Carmelita, Sr. Delores, Sr. Loretta, Sr. Maria, Sr. June, Sr. Theresa, Sr. Mary Kelly—and so many others who served our parish and our community over the years (some of those years pre-dating me).

photograph by Stacey Gentry

I did not only sit and listen during Morning Mass. I was a participant, and when folks prayed, I was among them—

together with the sisters, the parishioners, and all the angels that spent time at our Mission.

photograph by Betty Lou Leaver

Very often, after morning Mass, I trotted over to the pathway between the church and the convent (the one that leads into town) and waited for my friend, Mary Anzar, who works at the gift shop and has taken care of me there since I was a kitten.

And I would follow her back to the gift shop, eager for the day to begin.

Remembering the
Mission Gift Shop

photograph by Stacey Gentry

photograph by Stacey Gentry

Right before the gift shop opens, the sun peers through the windows and bathes me in all the colors of the rainbow.

photograph by Stacey Gentry

The staff liked the way the sub bathed me in color so much that they made magnets of that picture to sell at the shop.

photograph by Stacey Gentry

At the gift shop, I have a friend, Luther. If you check out my Face Book page, you can see a video of him strutting across my work space at the gift shop. Our Mission welcomes all God's creatures, as do especially our priest and the Franciscan sisters. Luther not only visited me; he also often visited the convent, as did many other roosters (and hens).

Here is Luther, looking in the window at my bed when I lived in the gift shop—but I got up even before roosters to go to work at morning Mass.

photograph by Betty Lou Leaver

As I said, Luther not only visited me, but he also visited the convent. Here is the proof: a picture of him outside the convent.

photograph by Stacey Gentry

I have my very own sales corner at the gift shop, where visitors can buy my six (already!—I like to write) books. There is a book about the Mission for children who visit, a book about saints for confirmation students looking for a name, books about religious holidays (Christmas,

Easter, Day of the Dead—that one, *Día de Muertos*, is in Spanish), and my very first one, which got a lot of really nice reviews, *Surviving Cancer, Healing People: One Cat's Story*. All of them have pictures not only of me but also of the sisters. You can read more details about them at the end of this book.

There are also magnets, cards, and trinkets in my corner of the gift shop, featuring (blush) me!

photograph by Stacey Gentry

One of the things I really liked about working at the gift shop was all the people who stopped by not just to shop but also to say hello to me. Some of them gave super head rubs!

One couple from Georgia had come to tour California and had added me to their itinerary. Can you believe that?!

Remembering
the Mission

photograph by Stacey Gentry

photograph by Stacey Gentry

When I lived at the gift shop, I patrolled the beautiful Mission gardens every day. Sometimes, a docent would bring visitors through. Visitors were sometimes surprised to learn that the Mission had a cat on staff, and many would stop to pet me and take pictures. (That is how I got some of the pictures for my books.)

photograph by Stacey Gentry

Like the sisters, I liked to participate in all the activities of the Mission. The sisters were always everywhere, and so was I. We all especially liked the fiestas.

Here I am with my friends on Sunday after the Fiesta de Candelaria: Mayra Alvarez, Elisa Hernandez (holding Betito), Monica Lopez, Kenia Hernandez, Maribel Arriaga, Sophia Lopez, Camila Lopez, Victor Lopez, and Roberto Cortes. Instead of watching football, we were talking and singing hymns together. Most of them are even more famous than I am! I love being connected to the Mission where there is always a fiesta!

photograph by Stacey Gentry

Every year, as a minimum, we have a spring and a fall fiesta. Some years we have more fiestas. Party! Party!

The spring fiesta takes place on or near June 24. Can you guess why? That is the feast day of St. John the Baptist, or, in Spanish, of San Juan Bautista! A very important day for our town.

The fall fiesta takes place around September 16 (Mexican Independence Day, dating from 1810). That is the one I am celebrating in the picture.

photograph by Betty Lou Leaver

I suppose you could not call it a fiesta per se, but is not Thanksgiving sort of an American fiesta? Every Thanksgiving (well, until Covid struck), Old Mission San Juan Bautista offered a very, very well attended community Thanksgiving dinner. Of course, the sisters were always there. People so looked forward to seeing Sr. Mary Kelly (on the left in the photograph) and Sr. Delores (on the right) and all the other sisters and talking to them!

photograph by Stacey Gentry

There are important religious days, as well. I like to participate in them, too, and the sisters always did as well. I miss seeing them on these special days. Everyone does. They knew so much about the significance and history of these days, and they shared it.

In terms of the yearly calendar, Lent and Easter appear first. I am not good at fasting for Lent. After all, a sick kitty must eat to stay alive, but I am very happy to restrict my Friday diet to fish.

I like being with the parishioners on Ash Wednesday when they get their ashes. I used to get a preview since I was always around when people were preparing the church. I cannot be there any more (just like the sisters), but my memory is good (and I hope theirs is, too).

photograph by Anais Mora

Good Friday services include Stations of the Cross and adoration of the cross. I have always sat with the parishioners in adoration. That includes being with the sisters, too. They were always present for Masses of every kind.

Long after everyone left, I would stay and adore the cross. That gave me some good alone time with my Boss, the good Lord, as well.

photograph by Stacey Gentry

An important church observance in our community is Day of the Dead. (I wrote a book about that—and our priest made sure it was completely accurate. So, if it is not an observance that you know much about, you can read details about it in my book—as long as you can read Spanish.)

I love Day of the Dead, especially the beautiful ofrenda, of which I am being a part in this picture. I think it is important to remember people who have passed on. I hope I will be remembered when my time comes.

photograph by Stacey Gentry

The Mission year always ended with Christmas, which is a beginning in a way, too, right? I am sure glad that the priest and the Franciscan sisters let me part of the Christmas celebration. The creche, you know, was originally created by St. Francis so I did think I belonged in it. He put animals into it, you know.

Remembering
the Farewell Mass
July 14, 2019

photograph by Betty Lou Leaver

photograph by Betty Lou Leaver

July 14, 2019 was a special day and a special Mass. It was the last Mass that the Franciscan Sisters of the Atonement in San Juan Bautista would attend at the Old Mission church. They departed for Graymoor the following Friday.

The Mission was packed. Everyone wanted to say goodbye.

The sisters sat on the left and up front, like they always did. Can you spot them? They are wearing Franciscan brown.

They are wearing... brown. (Hint: Sr. Maria, in dark brown, is holding a hymnal.)

Fr. Alberto called the sisters to the front of the church. The ladies in Franciscan brown are the sisters (Sr. Delores on the left and Srs. Carmelita and Mary Kelly on the right.) The lady in white is a parishioner, and she had something to say.

I just listened. I would miss them, and I hoped they would remember me. I know that the one they would miss most—and who would miss them most—was Julius. He had become part of their family at the convent. (No worries; the Mission staff followed up with Julius.)

photograph by Betty Lou Leaver

The mariachis are on the way! They came to Mass, too!
At the end, they proceeded down the aisle with inspiring
and toe-tapping music. So joyful! Franciscan-like, right?
Who does not feel joy from hearing the mariachis play
and sing?

For those who do not hail from my part of the world (or from elsewhere in the Californias or Mexico), you may not know about the wonders of mariachi music. Mariachi is a genre of regional Mexican music that dates back to at least the 18th century. Over time, it has evolved and migrated to new locations in Mexico and the Western USA. UNESCO has recognized it as being of cultural significance to Mexico, The music includes ballads and a wide variety of dances, as well as a wide range of lyrics— something for everybody.

photograph by Betty Lou Leaver

After Mass, the mariachis continued to play in the Mission gardens as Sr. Delores and others listened. And then the party commenced in the Mission gardens. Music continued to set the feet tapping, and everyone had a chance to picnic and say goodbye personally to the sisters.

photograph by Betty Lou Leaver

Finally, Sr. Delores got to talk to the mariachis. And we all got to talk to Sr. Delores and the other sisters. We knew we were going to miss them—and we do.

photograph by Betty Lou Leaver

The tables had been prepared in advance. The food was scrumptious. The people flocked to talk together and to say good-bye to the beloved sisters.

I wandered through the crowd, but no one took my picture. I was not the star of the day. The sisters were.

I especially liked the head table. I got to watch it being set up. I thought it was beautiful. I hope the sisters liked it.

Bon Voyage!

Photograph by Betty Lou Leaver

Here are Srs. Delories, Maria, and Carmelita with Fr. Ken, director of St. Francis Retreat Center. Fr. Ken, who grew up in San Juan Bautista, held a private, final Mass in the convent chapel on the day that the sisters departed

BON VOYAGE, SISTERS!
HAVE A WONDERFUL RETIREMENT!

More about Sula
and Her Works

photograph by Stacey Gentry

My Bio in the Words of Others

If a picture is worth a thousand words, you are in luck. You can read more stories about me and see more pictures here. There are even some places you can communicate with me—or come see me on a Sunday. The church is now too long a distance for my arthritic paws and tumored legs, but I do still come to the Gift Shop to meet with parishioners in need of cat care. (Please do check with the Gift Shop first; I will be completely retired soon because of health and because, well, everyone does eventually retire, right?). Do follow me on Face Book; that is the best way to be in contact with me.

California Newspapers

photographs by Nick Lovejoy

"A Cat's Mission." *Hollister Freelance* (Katie Helland, author; Nick Lovejoy/Studio Lovejoy, photographer). January 7 2016, pages B1, B15-16. http://www. sanbenitocountytoday.com/lifestyles/sula-the-cat-is-on-a-mission-in-san-juan/article_813c16f6-b575-11e5-886b-cfab711d8975.html

"Sula the Cat Is on a Mission in San Juan." *Morgan Hill Times* (Katie Helland). January 7, 2016. http://www. morganhilltimes.com/sula-the-cat/image_2a14d475-2f16-548a-a08d-62aa914fcd23.html (Yes, it is the same story—for different readers.)

photograph by Stacey Gentry

"San Juan Bautista Publisher Aids Local Mission with Unique Books by a Special Cat" (Melissa Jones). January 20, 2022. https://sanfranciscopost.com/san-juan-bautista-publisher-aids-local-mission-with-unqiue-books-by-a-special cat/.

Guideposts Publications

"Cat with a Divine Mission." (Elizabeth Mahlou). *Guideposts Magazine.* December 2015. Pages 60-63 in *Guideposts.*

photograph by Martin Klimek Photograph

"Family Room." *Guideposts Magazine.* December 2015, Pages 79-80.

"Sula, a Cat with a Divine Mission." https://www.guideposts.org/slideshow/sula-a-cat-with-a-divine-mission

"Cat with a Mission" was reprinted in *All Creatures* magazine as the feature story in the November-December 2017 issue.

Blog Posts

Interview with Mudpie. My interview with Mudpie, the Cat: http://www.mochasmysteriesmeows.com/2016/09/mudpie-interviews-sula-old-mission-san.html

MSI Press Blog. The MSI Press blog has a LOT of posts about me and my books. Check it out here: www.blogspot.

msipress.com; just type in the keyword, Sula.

Face Book

Follow my adventures on my Face Book page, Sula, by friending me. Or, just like me! https://www.facebook.com/Sula-909598572467537/. More pictures! More stories! And I will answer you!

Old Mission San Juan Bautista

Old Mission
San Juan Bautista

Parish Mission Statement
We are a welcoming Catholic community called by
God to spread the good news of Jesus Christ to all.

Founded June 24, 1797
By Fr. Fermín de Lasuén
15th of the 21 California Missions

Declaración
Somos una comunidad católica llamada por
Dios para llevar el mensaje de Jesucristo al mundo.

PARISH STAFF– EL PERSONAL

Pastor
fralberto@oldmissionsjb.org
(831)623-2127
Fr. Alberto Cabrera

Finance Manager
magda@oldmissionsjb.org
Magda Perino

Coordinator of Faith Formation & RCIA
Rosalba@oldmissionsjb.org
(831)623-4178
Rosa Garcia

Parish Secretary
daniela@oldmissionsjb.org
(831)623-2127
Daniela Desiderio

Gift Shop Supervisor/ Tours
Rocio@oldmissionsjb.org
(831)623-4528
Rocio Bastardo

Mission Ambassador
benito@oldmissionsjb.org
(831)623-4528
Benito Garcia

Gift Shop Clerks
(831)623-4528
Mary Anzar,
Hilda Farias

Gardener
Juan Ceja

Housekeeping
Anabel Perez

Casa Maria Hall
(831)623-2127
magda@oldmissionsjb.org
Magda Perino

Mission Cat
Sunday Visits
Sula

First Sunday of Advent
November 28, 2021

P.O. Box 400 (406 Second Street)
San Juan Bautista, CA 95045
Phone: 831-623-2127

MASS SCHEDULE
English Masses
Daily Mass Wednesday—Friday
8:00 a.m.
Saturday Vigil 5:00 p.m.
Sunday 8:30 a.m. and 10 a.m.

Confession Fridays at 5PM or by
appointment

HORARIO DE MISA
Misas en español
Domingo 12:00 p.m. y 1:30 p.m.

Confesiones los viernes
a las 5:00 p.m. o por cita

Parish Office - Oficina Parroquial
831-623-2127 Fax: 831-623-2433
Mon.-Fri.: 9:00 am - 4:00 pm (closed 12-1 p.m.)
Sundays: 9:00 a.m.-1:00 p.m.
www.oldmissionsjb.org

Office of Faith Formation– Catecismo
831-623-4178

Mission Store & Visitor Center– Tienda
831-623-4528
Open Wed.– Sunday from 9:00-4:00

Other Books by Me

My books are available at bookstores, online, and at Old Mission San Juan Bautista and St. Francis Retreat Center in San Juan Bautista. They can be purchased at discount (use code FF25) at the MSI Press webstore (www.msipress. com/shop). You may also be able to find them in your local library or bookstore.

My Published Books

photograph by Stacey Gentry

Christmas at the Mission

In December 2017, I wrote my first holiday book, called *Christmas at the Mission: A Cat's View of Catholic Customs and Beliefs.* I had a lot of fun writing it, learned a lot about Christmas and the source of Catholic customs, and delighted in the ways that Zhenya Yanovich, the Russian artist who illustrated the book, included me in each and every custom!

Book description from Amazon: Sula the Cat does it again! Sula, parish cat at Old Mission San Juan Bautista, is a cat with a special mission: to comfort people in need. Every morning, she spends time with St. Francis, patron saint of animals, and receives guidance for the day. During Masses, led by the Holy Spirit, she seeks out whomever God wants her to comfort, and they report that she brings comfort, indeed. In her spare time, she writes books. This time, she is writing about Christmas traditions and how she experiences them as a parish cat. Ever wonder where our various Christmas customs come from? Sula tells you about the history and the customs today, both mainstream American Catholic and Mexican American Catholic customs since both are part of her parish in California. Charmingly illustrated with an Eastern flavor by Russian artist, Zhenya Yanovich.

cover photograph by Stacey Gentry

Día de Muertos

Finally, after five other books, I gave in to requests from the first-language-Spanish speakers (we have lots of them at the Mission) who wanted a book in Spanish. Day of the Dead, which is a very popular commemoration at the

Mission, seemed more appropriately written in Spanish, so I did it. Of course, I had a lot of help from Spanish-speaking staff at the Mission and Spanish-speaking friends. And I had really big help from Fr. Alberto who made sure both the content and the language were correct.

Book description from Amazon: El Día de Muertos es una celebración muy importante, popular y solemne en San Juan Bautista, California, y en la Antigua Misión de San Juan Bautista, una de las misiones establecidas por los frailes franciscanos cuando se fundó California, y hogar de la gata parroquial, Sula. La comida, la oración y el recuerdo son parte de la celebración, al igual que las procesiones al cementerio.

Sula es la gata muy querida de la Antigua Misión de San Juan Bautista, California, donde ministra a los feligreses y visitantes diariamente, una labor divina. Este libro es su sexto.

English translation: Day of the Dead is an important secular and sacred celebration in San Juan Bautista, California and at Old Mission San Juan Bautista, one of the Missions established by the Franciscan friars and home to parish cat, Sula. Food, prayer, and remembrances are part of the celebration, as are processions to the cemetery. Sula is the beloved cat of the Mission, where she ministers to parishioners and visitors daily. This book is her sixth.

photograph by Stacey Gentry
cover photograph by Anais Mora

Easter at the Mission

A couple of years ago, I wrote about Easter. It seemed the proper thing to do since I had already written about Christmas. The beginning and the end. That seemed like a good way to bookend my books, but I did not stop there. I keep writing because people keep asking—and they have all kinds of ideas for topics.

Book description from Amazon: Sula, the now-famous church cat, tackles a mysterious topic for her fifth book: What is Easter, what is its meaning, what are the beliefs behind Catholic behaviors associated with the Lenten season and Easter, why is it called the Paschal mystery?

Sula answers these questions with history, dogma, and humor. And, of course, with pictures, lots and lots of people-cat pictures.

The sections of the book—Ash Wednesday, Lent, Palm Sunday, Holy Thursday, Good Friday, Easter Vigil and Easter Morning—are beautifully illustrated with drawings by Uliana Yanovich.

cover photograph by Betty Lou Leaver

Saints I Know

This book was written especially for kids in catechism classes. I hope it will help them find their confirmation name. Even if not that, I hope it will help them understand the saints better.

I can share a secret about this book.

You can read about their early lives and how they became saints. They were not always perfect, you know. And look at the last chapter—I make a prediction about future saints! Some of them may look familiar!

Book description from Amazon: A description of the lives of 21 saints--in both their imperfection and perfection--chosen based on the relationship to a Franciscan Mission, Old Mission San Juan Bautista, told through the eyes of the Mission's cat. The sections of the book including saints related to the founding of the mission (St. Francis, St. John the Baptist, and St. Juniper Serra), the Holy parents (Mary and Joseph), saints whose statues are behind the altar in the Mission, patron saints of animals, patron saints of children, and the favorite saints of the parish priest. A final section addresses future saints.

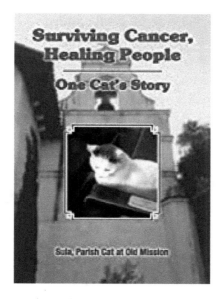

(cover design by Carl D. Leaver)

Surviving Cancer, Helping People: One Cat's Story

This is my first, best known, and apparently best loved book. I wrote this book to share my experiences in surviving cancer. I am now a six-time survivor! Well, five-time survivor. Cancer has struck again! I am fighting, but I am not as young as I used to be.

Book description from Amazon: A cat with a divine mission, Sula has an uncanny ability to sense which parishioners at Old Mission San Juan Bautista (California) need her attention at any given Mass. But...is it really uncanny, or does St. Francis give Sula tasks during her daily conversations with him? Or is she led by God? Sula has developed a special bond with cancer survivors like herself. The bond between her and the Old Mission parishioners saw her through two bouts of cancer, flooding her with gifts: money for surgery, a home for recovery, prayers, and love. In these pages, you will find charming, endearing, and inspiring stories, shared by parishioners and told from the point of view of a lovable and amazingly insightful cat. Once you open this book, you will not close it!

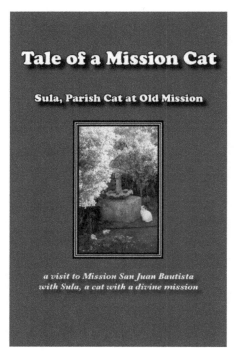

Tale of a Mission Cat

Here is a secret I can share about this book. I wrote it for fourth-graders, but anybody can read it. You see, fourth-graders in California, for their social studies classes, have to visit one of the 21 missions and write a report on it. Many choose mine, and during the week, you can find our Mission grounds saturated with curious kids. They stop and pet me, and they follow on tours to learn about our mission. There is a lot, though, that cannot go into a quick tour and or into handouts. That is what I put into Tale of a Mission Cat—the extra, fun information that visitors might not otherwise know about. With pictures, of course!

My second book, *Tale of a Mission Cat*, was written mainly for children. As it turned out, kids come in all ages, and many really big kids read this book. In the book, I introduce readers to Old Mission San Juan Bautista, my home—the church, the grounds, and the history.

Book description from Amazon: Sula, parish cat at Old Mission San Juan Bautista has written her second book about life at the Mission from a cat's point of view--a special cat, that is, with a mission from God to take care of parishioners. In this book, meant for children, Sula describes her work at the Mission, the parts of a Catholic Mission, and the Catholic faith. She pulls from contemporary experience as well as from the history of the Missions. Beautiful, hard-to-find pictures are sure to delight children of all ages.

My Works in Progress

Finding God in Adversity

After I wrote my book about surviving and all the things that having cancer taught me, people started asking me to write books about other difficult things. I figured they all fall into that category, called adversity. So, as soon as I get a chance, I will write a book just for them—because they asked.

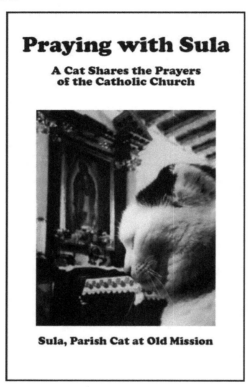

Praying with Sula

A Cat Shares the Prayers of the Catholic Church

Sula, Parish Cat at Old Mission

Praying with Sula

I had such fun writing all these books that I don't want to stop. I am working on a book about Franciscan prayers. (Come on, I could not possibly include all Catholic prayers. We Catholics are very prolific when it comes to prayer.) And I explain the prayers. I want this book to be both informative and helpful. After all, prayer is how I talk to my Boss and how the parishioners talk to Him, too. That is one of the most important things in the world and in life. Oh, and if plans work out, the book will be bilingual, English and Spanish. Here in San Juan Bautista both languages and cultures are equally important.

What People Say about My Books

Surviving Cancer, Healing People: One Cat's Story

Surviving Cancer, Healing People: One Cat's Story is comprised of truly charming, heartwarming, endearing, and inspiring stories, shared by parishioners and told from the point of view of a lovable and amazingly insightful cat. [This] is one of those books that will linger in the mind and memory of the reader long after it is finished and set back upon the shelf. Heartwarming and thoughtful, *Surviving Cancer, Healing People* is a joy to browse and highly recommended.

Reviewers' Choice/Small Press Bookwatch/Midwest Book Review

Once you meet Sula through the pages of this book, you won't soon forget her. While it's Sula's "meowmoir," it's also the story of those whose lives she's impacted and an inside look at California's Spanish mission. Whether you're a religious person or not, the history is fascinating, and the connection she has with the people she's drawn to is undeniable. I've always said if there is such a thing as angels on earth, they come in the form of fur and four legs; at least, I know that's how they've always presented themselves in my own life. Sula is further proof of what I've suspected all along.

Melissa's Mochas, Mysteries, and Meows blog

The inscription "Hic domus dei est et porta coeli," which means "This is the house of God and the gateway to heaven" towers over the portal to the church of Old Mission San Juan Bautista, greeting all who enter. But if guests happen to glance down, they might see a slightly rotund white cat with black markings and no ears. This would be Sula, the mission cat decreed by God, who he calls his Boss, to welcome all to the mission and to comfort those who are hurting. Sula knows about pain because he suffered through two bouts of cancer, having lost his ears in the process. *Surviving Cancer, Healing People: One Cat's Story* by Sula Parish Cat at Old Mission was written and photographed by staff and friends of the mission, but cleverly presented in the voice of Sula. As we learn about Sula, we also learn about the mission as well as St. Francis' Friars Minor and the Sisters of Atonement. As a tourist destination, the mission calls to all to come to the table and worship. To quote Fr. Jerry from Sula, "the Table is ready, and all are invited." *Surviving Cancer, Healing People: One Cat's Story* was written to raise funds for the Old Mission San Juan Bautista. Because the over-200-year-old mission sits on top of the intersection of three fault lines, earthquakes have struck twice in the past and each tremor has weakened it. Beyond being a fundraiser, though, the book is an inspirational call to worship. This little book about Sula, the mission cat, not only weaves short sermons into each chapter, but gives a short history of the mission of San Juan Bautista. We learn why cat doors were installed, why the church doors were built so high, and why the church was arranged around the sun of the winter solstice. Thanks to the great writing, photography and editing, the book flows nicely and leaves the reader with a positive and peaceful feeling. Loved this little book! I want to go to the mission now and visit with Ms. Sula in person. I highly recommend this sweet little book to all readers.

Claudia Coffey (Readers' Favorite)

I LOVED this book and highly recommend it. Sula the cat lives at Old Mission in California, a Franciscan mission which needs many repairs from past earthquakes and to secure it for another one. The book is part of a fundraiser for those efforts. Sula takes her job very seriously at the mission. She visits a statue of St. Francis every day where she learns of what her duties are that day and who needs her the most. She then enters the church and sits with those people during mass. As a Catholic (somewhat lapsed) I enjoyed reading about the mass, but you don't have to be any particular religion to read this. Sula is mainly white and the California sun has not been good to her. She has had to have surgery for cancer on her ears twice so she doesn't have ears anymore, but that doesn't stop her from loving everyone and everyone loving her.

15 and Meowing blog

There have always been cats living at the Old Mission San Juan Bautista. It is one of twenty-one Spanish missions in southern California built by the Franciscan order. Round holes were cut into its heavy doors during construction. Early cats were welcomed to hunt mice, but the current parish cat, Sula, has been tasked with a different mission.

Every day this big, white Turkish Van cat reports to the garden statue of St. Francis of Assisi, a lover of all animals... and people. In this book, Sula claims to receive orders concerning which church visitors need the comfort of a cat companion on any given day. Regardless of how she recognizes her charges, Sula instinctively approaches someone in need. It might be a communicant taking confession for the last time before joining her departed spouse. It may be visitors who arrive at the mission in time for a mass. She sits quietly at their feet or climbs onto a lap. Perhaps it is someone who has read Sula's story online and has come to meet and pet this now famous cat. Why is she famous? Sula is a cancer survivor. She has lost both ears due to melanoma skin cancer and resulting surgeries. (Two parishioners took care of her during that time.) Like any human might, Sula enjoys spending a great deal of time outside in the bright California sun. Being a survivor, she now attracts people who have or did have cancer themselves. The mission's gift shop office is Sula's official place of residence. The team there has encouraged the telling of her story, and that of some parishioners, in books and magazine articles.

Donna Ford (US Review of Books; Recommended)

I loved this book. Sula the cat lives at a mission in California. She visits a statue of St. Francis daily where she learns who she should spend time with that day. She goes in the church during mass time and visits with those she senses could use some love. She also visits with people in the gift shop and on field trips. Poor Sula has lost her ears from skin cancer, but that doesn't make her any less lovable. The mission has been through earthquakes and is in need of repairs if it is to stay standing through another one. Sula wrote this book to help raise funds for this. If you love cats, you will definitely love this book.

Ellen Pitch (Goodreads)

A Wise and Eminently Sane Cat, May 5, 2017. Sula is a feline inhabitant of the Old Mission San Juan Bautista in California. Her personal mission is to bring comfort and reassurance to those who need to experience God's love in a tangible way. She selects individuals in the church and sits by them or on their laps during services. She accompanies visitors as they tour the grounds or walk the stations of the cross. This charming book is full of lovely photos of Sula fulfilling her mission as well as her reflections as she does so. Sula is wise and eminently sane. She has learned to grieve (for the loss of her ears due to cancer) without becoming stuck in grief. She has learned the joy of helping others and lovingly seeks to offer comfort and aid whenever she can. At the same time, she has learned to gratefully accept help when she is in need. She has learned to look for silver linings in the darkest clouds. When she had to wear a cone after her cancerous ears were removed, she was forced to find unusual ways of eating from her bowl. Sula said this helped her to understand that physically and mentally handicapped parishioners face additional challenges and also need to find alternative ways of doing things. The experience increased her acceptance and understanding of others. Her faith is strong and she trusts her maker. The Old Mission surrounds her with reminders of His love and care. She is grateful and content. Her example serves as a reminder to seek the things that can make us truly joyful. I would love to have a friend like Sula.

Charles Lord (Amazon review)

Sweet Cat on a mission to save a Mission, August 22, 2016. I loved this book. This is a memoir of sorts written by Sula, a cat that lives at a mission in California. She takes her work of communing with people very seriously. All day, every day she spends visiting with people in the church, gift shop and walking around the mission grounds. The California sun has been harsh on her. Poor Sula has had surgery twice to remove cancer on her ears. Despite no longer having ears, she is still adorable and loving. The mission has been around a long time, through many earthquakes which has weakened the structure. Sula has written this book to raise funds to help do the work necessary to keep it from falling down. This book is a must read for all cat lovers. I know all Catholics would enjoy it as well, but that is not a requirement to read it :)

Amazon customer (Amazon review)

Tale of a Mission Cat

Remarkable Sula! Love that Supercat!

Kris Maas (Sula fan)

All reader reviews have been 5 stars! Thank you, readers!

Letter to the Reader

Dear Reader,

My mission is to write books in order to raise money to help my Mission repair itself, like my mentor St. Francis worked to repair God's church. I understand that my books have raised thousands of dollars toward that goal, but our Preservation Committee has a big task. We have also to retrofit the Mission to withstand earthquakes. It was damaged in 1906 and 1954 from earthquakes, and it sits at the crossroads of three faults. Making our Mission safe for all who come to us is estimated to cost $14 million. Ulp! I am going to keep writing and writing! That is my contribution to the preservation fund.

You can help, too.

- If you have some spare pennies, you can send a check made out to Old Mission San Juan Bautista Preservation Fund to

  Old Mission San Juan Bautista
  P O Box 222
  San Juan Bautista, CA 95045

  If you note on it "in honor of Sula," I will be tickled pink (which is quite a thing for a white cat!).

- No pennies to pinch? Not everyone is in a position to contribute financially. I understand that. I am only a cat. I can only contribute through my book sales and people donating in my name. Nearly anyone can contribute in a big way that does not cost anything: tell other people about my books and about our fund—and about our fun fiestas and great concerts, which also raise money for the Mission.

Thank you so much for reading my book. I hope it brought you joy. Joy is what I found in my relationship with the Franciscan sisters.

Your friend,

Sula

photograph by Stacey Gentry

CPSIA information can be obtained
at www.ICGtesting.com
Printed in the USA
BVHW020319260822
645564BV00008B/131